ACHIEVE LEVEL 4

Grammar, Punctuation and Spelling

Revision and Practice

Louise Moore
Revisions by Maddy Barnes

RISING STARS

PLEASE NOTE: THIS BOOK MAY NOT BE PHOTOCOPIED OR REPRODUCED AND WE APPRECIATE YOUR HELP IN PROTECTING OUR COPYRIGHT.

Rising Stars UK Ltd, 7 Hatchers Mews, Bermondsey Street, London SE1 3GS
www.risingstars-uk.com

Every effort has been made to trace copyright holders and obtain their permission for the use of copyright material. The authors and publishers will gladly receive information enabling them to rectify any error or omission in subsequent editions.

All facts are correct at time of going to press.

© 2012
Published 2012
Reprinted 2012
Reprinted with revisions 2013
New edition printed 2013
Reprinted 2014 (three times), 2015

Text, design and layout © Rising Stars UK Ltd
Cover design: Burville-Riley Design
Design: David Blundell, Branford Graphics
Layout: Words & Pictures Ltd, London
Editorial: Dawn Booth
Proofreaders: Margaret Crowther and David Mantovani
Illustrations: Phill Burrows (People) and Emily Skinner

British Library Cataloguing in Publication Data
A CIP record for this book is available from the British Library.

ISBN: 978-0-85769-958-9

Printed by Craftprint International, Singapore

Contents

Answers are in the centre of the book and can be pulled out before handing to the child.

How to use this book

1 Important facts and skills are given at the top of each section. Read them carefully – they show what you really need to know.

2 There is an example question for you to read through. Follow the steps carefully, then try to work through the example yourself.

3 Top tips are given on many pages – they are hints to help you do your best and make learning easier and more fun. Use them well!

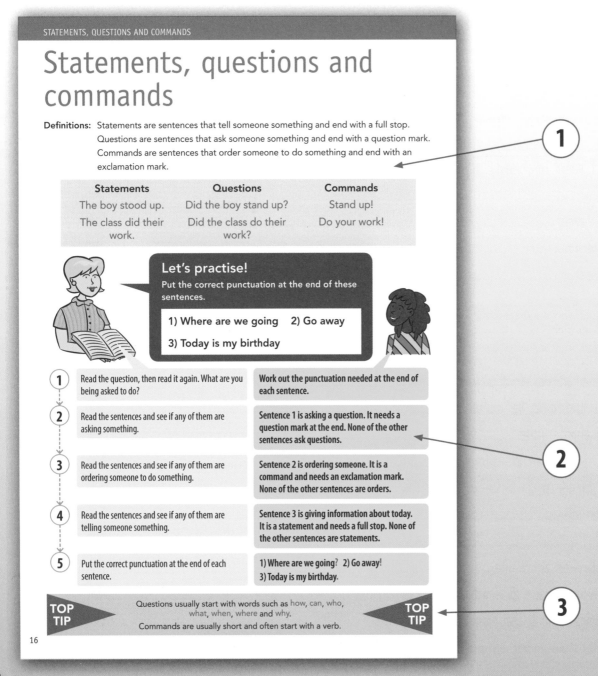

4 Each section has a set of practice questions. Each question has a space for you to write in the answer and a specific number of marks (as in a real National Test). Answers are included in the middle, although your teacher may remove these pages! Marking guidance is provided.

5 Questions are asked in lots of different ways to check that you really understand the topic.

6 If you feel confident with the topic, most sections finish with a challenge. This is a chance to push yourself a little bit further and see what you can achieve!

7 You will see an assessment panel at the top of each set of practice questions. Colour in the face that best describes your understanding of the topic and how you did. Use the words at the end of the book to help you learn and practise your spelling.

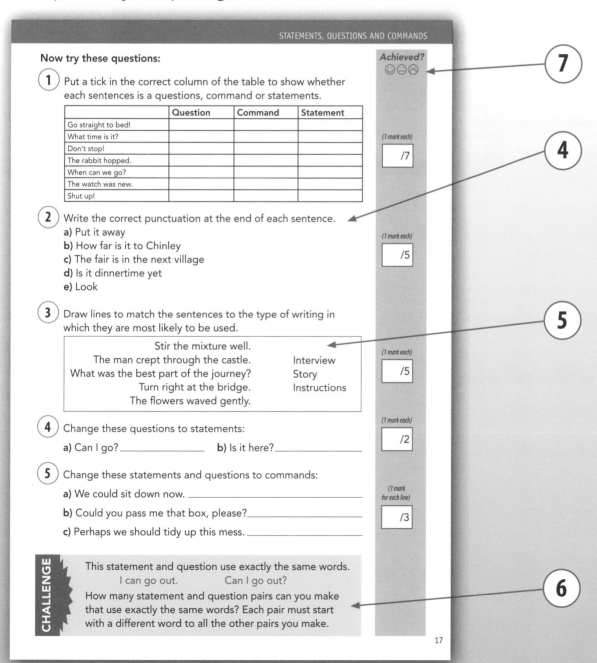

STATEMENTS, QUESTIONS AND COMMANDS

Now try these questions:

1 Put a tick in the correct column of the table to show whether each sentences is a questions, command or statements.

	Question	Command	Statement
Go straight to bed!			
What time is it?			
Don't stop!			
The rabbit hopped.			
When can we go?			
The watch was new.			
Shut up!			

Achieved?
☺☹☹

(1 mark each)

/7

2 Write the correct punctuation at the end of each sentence.
a) Put it away
b) How far is it to Chinley
c) The fair is in the next village
d) Is it dinnertime yet
e) Look

(1 mark each)

/5

3 Draw lines to match the sentences to the type of writing in which they are most likely to be used.

Stir the mixture well.
The man crept through the castle.
What was the best part of the journey?
Turn right at the bridge.
The flowers waved gently.

Interview
Story
Instructions

(1 mark each)

/5

4 Change these questions to statements:
a) Can I go? _____ b) Is it here? _____

(1 mark each)

/2

5 Change these statements and questions to commands:
a) We could sit down now. _____
b) Could you pass me that box, please? _____
c) Perhaps we should tidy up this mess. _____

(1 mark for each line)

/3

CHALLENGE
This statement and question use exactly the same words.
I can go out.   Can I go out?
How many statement and question pairs can you make that use exactly the same words? Each pair must start with a different word to all the other pairs you make.

17

5

Nouns and adjectives

Definitions: Nouns name a person, animal, place, thing or idea.

Adjectives describe nouns.

Purposes: Proper nouns name specific people or places and start with a capital letter:

| France | James | London | Box Hill | Castleton |

Adjectives describe the quantity, quality, size, age, shape, colour, place of origin or purpose of a noun:

five **old** **men**   the old, square **tower**   a young French **tourist**

Let's practise!
Underline the noun and circle the adjective in this sentence.

An angry dog barked.

(1)	Read the question, then read it again. What are you being asked to do?	**Find the noun and adjective in this sentence.**
(2)	Look for the word that names something.	**Dog is the name of something – underline dog.**
(3)	Look for the word that describes the dog.	**Angry describes the dog – draw a circle around angry.**
(5)	Check the noun and adjective in your answer	**An (angry) dog barked.**

Now try these questions:

1 Sort these words into the correct boxes.

old   geese   frightened   Harry   airport
grey   five   triangular   coach   phone

(1 mark for every 2 correct)

Nouns	Adjectives

/5

2 What type of word is the word in bold in this sentence?
The car drove down the **bumpy** road.
Bumpy is used as an _____

(1 mark)

/1

3 What type of word is the word in bold in this sentence?
There was an open **door**.   **Door** is used as a _____

(1 mark)

/1

4 Circle the word that describes the town in this sentence.

The dragon flew over the crowded town.

(1 mark)

/1

5 In each of these sentences, underline the noun and circle the adjective.
a) The lazy postman never came.
b) An old bus broke down.
c) The silly boy shouted loudly.
d) A frightened rabbit looked around warily.

(1 mark for each line)

/4

6 In the boxes below, write **N** if the word is a noun or write **A** if the word is an adjective.

The hungry wolf circled the sleeping camp, looking for the weakest youngster.

(1 mark each)

/5

CHALLENGE

Can you find adjectives that describe the quantity, shape, quality, size, age, colour, place of origin or purpose of each of the following nouns? Write your ideas down clearly.

_____ houses   _____ men   _____ cars
_____ teachers   _____ pilots   _____ boxes

7

Verbs and adverbs

Definitions: Verbs give an action or happening.

Adverbs give more information about verbs.

Purposes: Verbs tell you what has happened, is happening or will happen.

He was asleep.	He is sleeping.	He will sleep.

Adverbs are words or groups of words that tell you how, when or where the action happened, is happening or will happen.

He will jump carefully.	I rode recklessly.	We are working outside.

-ly words
Lots of adverbs end in the letters -ly and that can be a good way to spot them!

easily	greedily	firmly

But beware
Not all adverbs end in -ly.

hard	far	late	fast

Let's practise!
In this sentence, underline the verb and circle the adverb.

The mysterious figure spoke softly.

1 Read the question, then read it again. What are you being asked to do?

Find the verb and adverb.

2 Look for the word that tells you what is happening in the sentence.

The figure spoke – that is what it did – so spoke is the verb.

3 Look for the word that tells you more about what is happening in the sentence.

It says the figure spoke softly so softly is the adverb.

4 Check the verb and adverb in your answer.

Check the verb and adverb in your answer. The mysterious figure spoke softly.

Now try these questions:

1 Write adverbs in each box to help describe the verb. The first one is done for you.

Verb	How?	When?	Where?
ran	*quickly*	*yesterday*	*uphill*
will fly			
slept			
listens			
ate			

(1 mark for every 3 correct)

/4

2 Sort these words into the correct boxes.

rapidly   fiercely   collected   calculates

happily   soon   hold   ran

Verbs	Adverbs

(1 mark for every 2 correct)

/4

3 What type of word is the word in bold in this sentence?
The man drove **recklessly**.   **Recklessly** is used as an _____

(1 mark)

/1

4 What type of word is the word in bold in this sentence?
Gary **laughed** like a hyena.   **Laughed** is used as a _____

(1 mark)

/1

5 Circle the word in this sentence that describes how the dragon flew.

The dragon flew gracefully over the distant hills.

(1 mark)

/1

6 In each sentence, underline the verb and circle the adverb.
a) The whistle blew shrilly.
b) The train arrived late.
c) Hastily, he hid the box.
d) They argued angrily about the broken phone.

(1 mark for each line)

/4

7 In the boxes below write **V** if the word is a verb or write **A** if the word is an adverb.

☐   ☐   ☐   ☐

Sadly, she walked past the canal boat, which was slowly sinking.

(1 mark each)

/4

CHALLENGE

Try to find interesting and unusual verbs and adverbs for each letter of the alphabet. Use your dictionary to help you and write your ideas down.

Pronouns

Definition: A pronoun is a word that takes the place of a noun in a sentence.

Purpose: To avoid having to repeat the names of things.

Style: Used in all writing styles.

Some words that can be used as pronouns:

I	you	he	she	we
they	it	her	him	us
them	mine	ours	theirs	his
hers	our	this	that	

Let's practise!
Underline the pronoun in this sentence and say what noun it is replacing.

> Isidore finished his bike ride early.

1 Read the question, then read it again. What are you being asked to do?

Find the word that is the pronoun.

2 Think what a pronoun does.

A pronoun replaces the name of something.

3 Which word replaces the name of something?

It must be the word his.

4 What is this pronoun replacing?

In the sentence the he is Isidore, so his must mean that it's Isidore's bike ride.

5 Check your answer in the sentence.

Isidore finished Isidore's bike ride early. It is repetitive but it makes sense.

6 This is the correct answer.

Isidore finished <u>his</u> bike ride early.

Now try these questions:

1 Underline the pronouns in the following sentences:

a) The cat saw it first.

b) Mary gave them to him.

c) She walked across the road when it was clear.

d) Despite the rain, they still went out on their bikes.

e) Whenever it stopped, he stood at the window.

f) Despite seeing her, he still told them that she had left.

(1 mark for each line)

/6

2 Cross out all the words in these sentences that could be replaced by pronouns. Write in the correct pronouns.

a) Toby told Tom that the door was locked.

b) Max lifted the boxes onto the table.

c) Olivia waved goodbye as Liam drove away in the car.

d) "Where is Lani's phone?" Isidore asked.

e) William and I went on the bus.

(1 mark for each line)

/5

3 Circle the correct pronoun to complete the following sentences correctly.

a) Anuerin put (his   he's   him   he) hand up first.

b) Jake took (she   me   their   it) letter to the post.

c) Give Kita (it   your   me   ours) phone.

d) Why did (its   her   their   they) arrive late?

(1 mark each)

/4

CHALLENGE

How many ways can you replace these pronouns in the following sentence to make exciting sentences?

They left **it** on top of **that**.

11

Connectives and conjunctions

Definitions: Connectives link different phrases, sentences and paragraphs together.
Conjunctions are connectives used to link different ideas in a sentence.

Examples of connectives:

> because of this   as well as   in addition   instead of   for example
> especially   however   despite   at the same time   finally
>
> Initially, Tom wanted to buy the phone. However, when he saw the price he knew it was too expensive. In addition, he heard that it was not very reliable. Consequently, he bought a cheaper phone that he knew would work well.

Examples of conjunctions:

> after   before   unless   although   if   until   as   since
> when   because   than   while   and   or   but
>
> Although it was raining, he still went to the football match.
>
> We walked until we reached a river. He can come out if he finishes his work.

Let's practise!

Complete the sentence with the appropriate connective.

> I got the highest mark _____ I won the competition.

1	Read the question, then read it again. What are you being asked to do?	Choose a connective that completes the sentence.
2	Check how the meaning of the two parts of the sentence relate to each other.	The second part happened because of the first part.
3	Think of connectives that show one thing that causes another to happen.	The first thing had to happen so the second one could happen. So is the connective we need.
4	Check the connective in the answer.	I got the highest mark <u>so</u> I won the competition.

 **TOP TIP**   All conjunctions are connectives.
They are connectives linking things within one sentence.   **TOP TIP**

Now try these questions:

1 Match these sentence openings to the best endings.

I was selected to run the race.

a) I ran the fastest although

my eyes are blue.

b) I ran the fastest because

my shoes didn't fit properly.

c) I ran the fastest so

I had trained the hardest.

(1 mark each)

/3

2 Complete each sentence with a suitable connective.

a) Harry was tired _____ he hadn't done a lot of work.

b) Annabelle tore her dress _____ she squeezed through the hedge.

c) Lewis went to school _____ really he wanted to go fishing.

d) Caitlin woke up early _____ she saw the sunrise.

(1 mark each)

/4

3 Circle the connectives in this paragraph.

John decided to hide his book before his mum asked him about his homework. When his mum asked, he told her that there wasn't any homework. Despite this, his mum was suspicious and went to phone Izzi, his friend, to check. Meanwhile, John remembered that if he didn't hand in his homework he would miss running club. Now what was he going to do?

(1 mark each)

/6

4 Complete these sentences.

a) Mr Wright was angry even though _____ .

b) Anuerin fell down the stairs because _____ .

c) Emanuela drew the picture while _____ .

d) Charlie knew she was late so _____ .

e) Before he went to bed _____ .

(1 mark each)

/5

CHALLENGE

Write down as many connectives as you can.

Can you find ways to group your connectives?

13

Prepositions

Definitions: Prepositions show the position of things.

Examples:

above	behind	below	beneath	between	by	down
in	inside	into	near	next to	off	on	onto
opposite	outside	over	through	under	underneath	upon

The bike was inside the shed, next to an old wheelbarrow and in front of the bench.

Let's practise!

Circle the preposition in the following sentence.

> Jac put the rabbit into its hutch.

1 Read the question, then read it again. What are you being asked to do?

Identify the preposition.

2 Look which word in the sentence tells you about the position of something.

We are told where the rabbit is put – into its hutch.

3 Check the preposition in the answer.

Jac put the rabbit⟨into⟩its hutch.

Now try these questions:

1 Match these sentence openings to the best endings.
   a) The cat sat underneath   the fire.
   b) The cat sat next to   the rows of flowers.
   c) The cat sat between   the bed.

(1 mark each)

/3

2 Complete each sentence with a suitable preposition.
   a) Ona put the bottle_____the fridge.
   b) He parked the car_____the main gate.
   c) Max sat_____the bridge.
   d) Eleanor walked_____the hills.

(1 mark each)

/4

CHALLENGE Write a sentence using the largest number of prepositions you can without using the word and.

Articles

Definitions: Articles are always used with nouns and give information about a noun.

Examples:

a	used when the next word begins with a consonant	b c d f g h j k l m n p q r s t v w x y z
an	used when the next word begins with a vowel	a e i o u some words beginning with 'h' need 'an' before them, for example, 'an hour', 'an honest decision'
the	can be used when the next word begins with a vowel or a consonant	

Let's practise!

Insert the article **a** or **an** in the sentence below.

You must complete____application form before you can apply for____ job here.

1 Read the question, then read it again. What are you being asked to do?

Identify which articles are needed.

2 Look at the word that follows the first line.

Application begins with a vowel sound so we need to write **an** before it.

3 Look at the word that follows the second line.

Job begins with a consonant sound so we need to write **a** before it.

4 Check the articles in your answers.

You must complete **an** application form before you can apply for **a** job here.

Now try these questions:

1 Write the correct article before these words. Choose from a or an.

a)_____arrow   b)_____gate   c)_____house

d)_____hour   e)_____engine   f)_____orange

(1 mark each)

/6

2 Circle the article in each of the sentences below.

a) Vishnu wanted a new cable for his laptop.

b) Some children needed an hour or two to complete their task.

c) The reason I forgot was because I was rushing.

d) Sarah had forgotten the password for her email account.

(1 mark each)

/4

15

Statements, questions and commands

Definitions: Statements are sentences that tell someone something and end with a full stop. Questions are sentences that ask someone something and end with a question mark. Commands are sentences that order someone to do something and end with an exclamation mark.

Statements	Questions	Commands
The boy stood up.	Did the boy stand up?	Stand up!
The class did their work.	Did the class do their work?	Do your work!

Let's practise!
Put the correct punctuation at the end of these sentences.

1) Where are we going   2) Go away

3) Today is my birthday

1 Read the question, then read it again. What are you being asked to do?

Work out the punctuation needed at the end of each sentence.

2 Read the sentences and see if any of them are asking something.

Sentence 1 is asking a question. It needs a question mark at the end. None of the other sentences ask questions.

3 Read the sentences and see if any of them are ordering someone to do something.

Sentence 2 is ordering someone. It is a command and needs an exclamation mark. None of the other sentences are orders.

4 Read the sentences and see if any of them are telling someone something.

Sentence 3 is giving information about today. It is a statement and needs a full stop. None of the other sentences are statements.

5 Put the correct punctuation at the end of each sentence.

1) Where are we going?   2) Go away!
3) Today is my birthday.

TOP TIP
Questions usually start with words such as how, can, who, what, when, where and why.
Commands are usually short and often start with a verb.

TOP TIP

16

Now try these questions:

Achieved?
☺☺☹

1 Put a tick in the correct column of the table to show whether each sentence is a question, command or statement.

	Question	Command	Statement
Go straight to bed!			
What time is it?			
Don't stop!			
The rabbit hopped.			
When can we go?			
The watch was new.			
Shut up!			

(1 mark each)

/7

2 Write the correct punctuation at the end of each sentence.
a) Put it away
b) How far is it to Chinley
c) The fair is in the next village
d) Is it dinnertime yet
e) Look

(1 mark each)

/5

3 Draw lines to match the sentences to the type of writing in which they are most likely to be used.

Stir the mixture well.
The man crept through the castle.
What was the best part of the journey?
Turn right at the bridge.
The flowers waved gently.

Interview
Story
Instructions

(1 mark each)

/5

4 Change these questions to statements:

a) Can I go? _____   **b)** Is it here?_____

(1 mark each)

/2

5 Change these statements and questions to commands:

a) We could sit down now. _____

b) Could you pass me that box, please?_____

c) Perhaps we should tidy up this mess. _____

(1 mark for each line)

/3

CHALLENGE

This statement and question use exactly the same words.
I can go out.   Can I go out?
How many statement and question pairs can you make that use exactly the same words? Each pair must start with a different word to all the other pairs you make.

Tenses

Definitions: Verbs can be written in the past, present or future tense.

The past tense shows that something has already happened.

The present tense shows that something is happening now.

The future tense shows that something will happen after now.

Examples:

Verb	Past	Present	Future
to listen	listened	listen(s)	will listen
to sleep	slept	sleep(s)	will sleep
to think	thought	think(s)	will think

Let's practise!

Choose the correct ending for this sentence.

The bike got a puncture after I

a) ride over the broken glass.

b) will ride over the broken glass.

c) rode over the broken glass.

d) riding over the broken glass.

1 Read the question, then read it again. What are you being asked to do?

Work out the ending that matches the start of the sentence.

2 Read the sentence and work out the tense.

The bike got a puncture – **this is telling what has happened, so it is in the** past **tense.**

3 Check the tense of the sentence endings.

a) ride over the broken glass – **is in the** present **tense.**

b) will ride over the broken glass – **is in the** future **tense.**

c) rode over the broken glass – **is in the** past **tense.**

d) riding over the broken glass – **is in the** present **tense.**

4 Find the ending that is the same tense as the beginning of the sentence.

c) is the only ending in the past **tense.**

5 Write the end on the sentence.

The **bike got a puncture after I** rode over the broken glass.

Now try these questions:

1 Complete the table. The first one is done for you.

Past tense	Present tense	Future tense
I drove / was driving	*I drive / am driving*	*I will drive*
he ate / was eating		
		we will watch
she jumped / was jumping		
	they work / are working	
		you will buy

(1 mark for each correct row)

/5

2 Change these sentences to the past tense.
a) I will go to school. _____
b) He is racing John. _____
c) I can see the moon. _____

(1 mark each)

/3

3 Change these sentences to the future tense.
a) Jake was late. _____
b) Caitlin is running well. _____
c) Stephi wanted a drink. _____

(1 mark each)

/3

4 Change these sentences to the present tense.
a) I will watch the film. _____
b) I heard a shout. _____
c) I taught Rowan to play the piano.

_____

(1 mark each)

/3

5 Match the verbs to the tense.

will laugh   hoped   waved   plead

fly

kicked

| past tense | present tense | future tense |

will sew

walk

climbed   grew   will dance   work

(1 mark for every 3 correct)

/4

6 Circle the correct ending for this sentence.
They decided to go swimming after
a) they will go to the shops.   **b)** they are going to the shops.
c) they had been to the shops.   **d)** they would go to the shops.

(1 mark)

/1

 **CHALLENGE**   How many sentences can you write that use all three tenses: past, present and future?

Subject and verb agreement

Definitions: The subject is who or what the sentence is about.

The verb is what the subject is doing.

Remember! **The subject and verb must agree.**

If there is one subject, the verb must be singular.

If there is more than one subject, the verb must be plural.

Examples:

The boy runs quickly.	There is only one boy so the singular verb is used.
The boys run quickly.	There is more than one boy so the plural verb is used.
The bears are angry.	There is more than one bear so the plural verb is used.

Let's practise!

Write **is** and **are** in the correct places in these sentences.

a) Jack _____ late.

b) Lucy and Libby_____ laughing.

c) Barti or William ——— doing it.

(1) Read the question, then read it again. What are you being asked to do?

Work out if the sentences need a singular or plural verb.

(2) Read each sentence and count the subjects.

a) Jack _____ late. There is only one subject – Jack. So we need the singular verb.

b) Lucy and Libby _____ laughing. There are two subjects – Lucy and Libby. So we need the plural verb.

c) Barti or William _____ doing it. There is only one subject – only Barti or William is doing it, not both of them. So we need the singular verb.

(3) Check which verb is singular and which is plural.

Use he to check for the singular verb and they to check for the plural verb.

Singular: He is. ✔ He are. ✗

Plural: They is. ✗ They are. ✔

(4) Write the singular and plural verbs in the correct sentences.

a) Jack is late. b) Lucy and Libby are laughing. c) Barti or William is doing it.

Now try these questions:

1 Complete the table.

Singular verb: He	swims	plays		races	holds	
Plural verb: They			write			catch

(1 mark for every 2 boxes correct)

/3

2 Tick the sentences that are correct.
a) There is two cars parked in front of me.
b) Max and Olli have finished their model.
c) Isabella or Cindy are going to do it.
d) Where is the money?
e) Robert spends all his time dreaming.
f) She listen carefully to the teacher.

(1 mark for each line)

/6

3 Circle one word that needs to be changed in each sentence.
a) Where is the cats?
b) I are here.
c) He arrive now.
d) The phone, which used to be ours, are ringing.
e) Harvey or Rio are up the ladder.
f) A guitar, a trumpet and a keyboard sounds good together.

(1 mark for each line)

/6

4 Complete the pictures to show the meaning of these sentences.

a) The sheep is on the road.   **b) The sheep are on the road.**

(1 mark each)

/2

5 Write these sentences correctly.
a) Joshua and George writes well. _____
b) The trees is too tall. _____
c) Where are the train? _____
d) Immi or the twins watches this programme. _____
e) Why is the children shouting? _____
f) The teenagers always shouts at me. _____

(1 mark for each line)

/6

CHALLENGE

Some verbs just take an s off the end to change from singular to plural. For example: He gazes.   They gaze.

How many verbs can you list that change in different ways? For example: He is.   We are.

21

I and me

Definition: Words that refer to yourself.

> I went to the football match.

> Show me how to do that!

The problem: When you talk about yourself with another person it can be tricky to know whether to use I or me.

> You and I went skating.

> You and me went skating.

The solution: Try the sentence just for yourself.

> I went skating.

> Me went skating.

Now it is easy to see which is correct – and that tells you which you need to use, so the correct sentence is:

> You and I went skating.

Let's practise!

Fill the blank correctly in this sentence using I or me.

The teacher gave the box to John and [   ] .

1 Read the question, then read it again. What are you being asked to do?

Work out whether **I** or **me** is the correct word to use in the sentence.

2 Take the additional person out of the sentence.

The teacher gave the box to _____ .

3 Test the sentence using I and me.

The teacher gave the box to I.
The teacher gave the box to me.

4 Choose the option that sounds correct.

The teacher gave the box to me.

5 Put your answer into the original sentence.

The teacher gave the box to John and me.

 **TOP TIP**   Remember to test the sentence as if it is just about yourself.   **TOP TIP**

Now try these questions:

1 Fill in the blanks correctly using I or me.

a) John and _____ jump.

b) He likes Sam and _____ .

c) Look where Alfie and _____ live.

(1 mark each)

/3

2 Tick the sentences that are correct.

Zia and I went fishing.	
Liam came with Conor and me.	
Lani and me ate pizza for dinner.	
They presented a cup to Laura and I.	
If Caitlin and I win, we will share the prize with Nye.	
Don't ask Eleanor and me to do the tidying up!	

(1 mark each)

/6

3 Fill in the blanks correctly using I or me.

a) Jake and _____ went to the disco.

b) The swimming pool is near where Max and _____ went walking.

c) Give the paints to Tom and _____ so we can finish our model.

d) Why do you and _____ always get the blame?

e) Thanks to you and _____ , that went really well.

(1 mark each)

/5

4 Fill in the blanks with either me or I, so that each sentence is correct.

a) My friend and _____ are here.

b) Why do you always blame Xia and _____?

c) Sam and _____ have finished.

d) Do you see the same problem as Cindy and _____ do?

e) Don't forget about Stephi and _____ .

(1 mark each)

/5

CHALLENGE

Make a set of ten cards with sentences using I and me. Make five of them correct and five incorrect. Challenge your friends and family to sort them.

Capital letters

Purposes: Capital letters are used in special cases.

For proper nouns: names of people, nationalities, languages, countries, places, days, months, religions, religious and public holidays		
To start a sentence	For the personal pronoun I	For the main words in titles

Let's practise!

Write this sentence with all the capital letters placed correctly.

> when i went to london last june, i went to the theatre to see a play called rising stars.

1 Read the question, then read it again. What are you being asked to do?

Put capital letters in the correct places.

2 Check that the sentence starts with a capital letter.

When i went to london last june, i went to the theatre to see a play called rising stars.

3 Check that the pronoun I is written with a capital letter.

When I went to london last june, I went to the theatre to see a play called rising stars.

4 Check for any proper nouns and write them with capital letters.

London and June are proper nouns. When I went to London last June, I went to the theatre to see a play called rising stars.

5 Check for any titles and write them with capital letters.

The play is called rising stars. We need to write Rising Stars.

6 Write the answer.

When I went to London last June, I went to the theatre to see a play called Rising Stars.

 **TOP TIP**

In titles, only put capitals on the main words. For example: *Harry Potter and the Philosopher's Stone, Lord of the Rings, Pride and Prejudice, Romeo and Juliet.*

TOP TIP

Now try these questions:

Achieved?
☺ ☺ ☹

1 Write three words correctly in each box.

Names of people	Names of cities	Names of countries	Names of religions
Names of days	Names of months	Names of books	Names of languages

(1 mark for every 3 correct)

/8

2 Circle the words that should be written with a capital letter.

john   stars   monday   paris   spanish   oak tree
beauty and the beast   canal   muslim   hammer   i   savoy hotel

(1 mark for every two correct capitals)

/5

3 Write these sentences with capital letters used correctly.
a) mr lomas was cross because last tuesday, at buxworth, we jumped in the canal.

_____

b) last july, the spanish students enjoyed performing in our concert, the sea saga.

_____

c) we walked up eccles pike when it snowed last christmas.

_____

d) when i talked to kim she said the diary of a dopey dog was her favourite book.

_____

(1 mark for 2 correct, 2 marks for 3 or more correct for each line)

/8

4 Cross out the capital letters that are not needed in these sentences.
a) Many Foxes live in towns and Cities, where they can Scavenge food from Bins.
b) Mrs Hartley caught a Train to London last Weekend.
c) One Day a Month we have a group talking about Religions at School.

(1 mark for each line)

/3

5 Circle the sentence that is correct.

Next, Pat went to the Hospital.	Next, pat went to the Hospital.
Next, Pat went to the hospital.	next, Pat went to the hospital.

(1 mark)

/1

CHALLENGE   Write your address correctly.

Question marks

Purposes: Question marks are used to punctuate a question

Some rules to consider:
- Make sure your question starts with a capital letter if it is a new sentence.
- When using direct speech, make sure your question mark is inside the inverted commas.

Let's practise!

Tick one box to show where the missing question mark should go.

"Do you know where the keys are" asked Dad.
☐ ☐ ☐

1 Read the question, then read it again. What are you being asked to do?

Tick the box where the question mark should go.

2 Read the sentence and identify the question.

Do you know where the keys are.

3 Check where the question mark should be.

The question mark should be at the end of the question. Do you know where the keys are?

4 Tick the box.

Tick the second box to show where the question mark should be.

Now try these questions:

Achieved?
☺ ☐ ☹

1 Write a suitable question to fit each answer. One has been done for you.

(1 mark each)

/2

Question	Answer
How old are you?	I am eleven years old.
	I went with my sister.
	It was amazing!

2 Read the sentences and insert a question mark if the sentence needs one.

(1 mark each)

/2

a) I have already shown you the newspaper, haven't I

b) "Didn't you realise it was non-uniform day Jack" whispered Abid.

26

Exclamation marks

Purposes: Exclamation marks are used to punctuate an exclamation or a command. For example: Stop! That was awful! Give it to me now! Wow! I don't believe this!

Some rules to consider:
- Use one exclamation mark to punctuate your sentences – you do not need multiple exclamation marks.
- When using direct speech, make sure your exclamation mark is inside the inverted commas.
- An exclamation mark replaces a full stop, do not use them together.

Let's practise!
Rewrite the sentence below, adding the missing exclamation mark.

> "Tidy up now" Miss Wileman shouted loudly.

1 Read the question, then read it again. What are you being asked to do?

Add the missing exclamation mark.

2 Think about what an exclamation mark is used for.

To punctuate an exclamation or a command.

3 Read the sentence and see if you can identify whether there is an exclamation or a command.

Tidy up now is a command so needs an exclamation mark.

4 Re-write the sentence.

"Tidy up now!" Miss Wileman shouted loudly.

Now try these questions:

Achieved?
☺ ☺ ☹

1 Tick the sentences which are punctuated correctly.
a) I can't believe we won! ☐
b) There are five apples! and three bananas in the bowl! ☐
c) Happy birthday! ☐

(1 mark each)

/3

2 Explain why an exclamation mark has been used in each of these sentences. One has been done for you.

Example	Explanation
a) Ouch!	To show a strong emotional response.
b) Open it!	
c) Unbelievable!	

(1 mark each)

/2

27

Commas

Purpose: Commas are used to break up a sentence.

You should be able to use commas in these ways:

- To separate more than two items in a list, instead of using the word and or or: I saw a kingfisher, a heron and some geese on the canal.
- To separate direct speech from the speaker: He said, "Let's go to the gym this week."
- In a complex sentence where the extra information (the dependent clause) comes first: Whenever I saw the shop, I thought about how much money I had spent.

Let's practise!

Put the commas in the correct places in this sentence.

> Paul asked "When we go to the theatre tonight can I have popcorn crisps and a coke?"

(1) Read the question, then read it again. What are you being asked to do?

Put the commas into the sentence.

(2) Check if there are any lists with more than two items.

popcorn crisps and a coke is a list with three items.

(3) Put commas where and or or could be written in the list.

We could write popcorn and crisps and a coke, so we put popcorn, crisps and a coke.

(4) Check if there is any direct speech that needs to be separated from the speaker.

We need to separate Paul from what he asked. Paul asked, "When we go to the theatre tonight can I have popcorn, crisps and a coke?"

(5) Check if there is a complex sentence that needs a comma.

When we go to the theatre tonight – is not a sentence on its own. Can I have popcorn, crisps and coke? – is a sentence on its own. The complete sentence doesn't come first, so we need a comma between the two.

(6) Write the complete answer.

Paul asked, "When we go to the theatre tonight, can I have popcorn, crisps and a coke?"

Now try these questions:

1 Insert the commas in these speech sentences, if they are needed.
a) "Come here!" shouted the angry farmer.
b) "The water is really cold" declared Tom.
c) Olivia asked "Why did you paint that red?"
d) "The film is starting" announced the usher.
e) Joshua whispered "I've forgotten my homework."

(1 mark for each line)

/5

2 Insert the commas where they are needed in these lists.
a) We packed shorts tee-shirts swimsuits and sandals.
b) He ate sandwiches crisps a pie some cherries and a biscuit.
c) We bought balloons streamers flags and bunting.
d) The house was big old dirty dark and cold.
e) A big red monster ate cars cans old rugs and an ironing board.

(1 mark for each line)

/5

3 Circle the sentences where the commas are used correctly.
a) John said, "Bring the oxygen tank."
b) After, he had stopped we went to the beach.
c) We went on the big wheel and the bumper cars and, the roundabout.
d) Suzy was an unhappy, worried and tired little girl.

(1 mark for each line)

/4

4 Cross out the unnecessary commas in these sentences.
a) Push, the button, and it will make a sound.
b) When I swim, I like, to splash, other people.
c) Sam said, "We don't, want to go."
d) Buy some milk, bread, and cheese, after tea.

(1 mark for each line)

/4

5 Put the commas where they are needed in these sentences.
a) "Have a good look" said Charlie "because you won't see it again."
b) To raise money for charity last night I walked ran swam and biked.
c) Bring the football in if you have finished playing.
d) Barti muttered "If we do maths literacy French and science I will be shattered!"
e) When he saw me he ran off down the road shouting "Help!"

(1 mark for each line)

/5

CHALLENGE Look in your reading book or a library book and see if you can work out any other ways that commas are used. List them along with the ones you already know.

Apostrophes

Uses:

To show omission/contraction	To show possession/ownership
To show where a letter or letters are missed out of a word (these words are called contractions) can't = can not she's = she is / she has he'd = he had / he would it's = it is	To show that something belongs to someone or something Lou's key the dog's bark the women's walk the boys' game

Remember! To show possession the rule is:

- if the word doesn't end in s then add 's   • if the word does end in s just add '
- EXCEPT you can add 's to words that end in s if you would say the double s. For example: James's shoes.

Let's practise!
Write the apostrophes correctly in this sentence.

> When Janes brothers arrived they werent sure where to find the boys changing room.

1 Read the question, then read it again. What are you being asked to do?	**Put the apostrophes in the correct places.**
2 Check if any words are contractions.	**werent** is a contraction of were not, **so should be written as** weren't.
3 Look for things that belong. Work out where they need an apostrophe.	**The** brothers **belong to** Jane. Jane **doesn't end with an** s **so we need to add** 's **to her name,** Jane's. **The** changing room **belongs to the** boys. **Boys ends with an** s **so we just add** ' **and write** boys'.
4 Write the sentence with all the apostrophes placed correctly.	**When** Jane's **brothers arrived they** weren't **sure where to find the** boys' **changing room.**

TOP TIP   Pronouns don't need apostrophes, so it's always means it is and its shows that something belongs to it.   **TOP TIP**

Answers

Page 7 Nouns and adjectives and articles

Question 1

Nouns	Adjectives
geese phone Harry airport coach	old frightened grey five triangular

Question 2 adjective

Question 3 noun

Question 4 (crowded)

Question 5 a) (lazy) postman. **b)** (old) bus **c)** (silly) boy **d)** (frightened) rabbit

Question 6

| A | | A | N |

The hungry wolf circled the sleeping camp, looking for the weakest youngster.

| A | N |

Challenge Answers will vary. Sample answers: big houses; large men; fast cars; good teachers; daring pilots; cardboard boxes.

Page 9 Verbs and adverbs

Question 1 Answers will vary. Sample answers:

Verb	How?	When?	Where?
will fly	directly	on Sunday	to Munich
slept	restlessly	on Christmas Eve	at his gran's
listens	carefully	in maths	at school
ate	hungrily	at breakfast	at the cafe

Question 2

Verbs	Adverbs
collected, calculates, hold, ran	rapidly, fiercely, happily, soon

Question 3 adverb

Question 4 verb

Question 5 (gracefully)

Question 6 a) blew (shrilly) **b)** arrived (late) **c)** (Hastily), hid **d)** argued (angrily)

| A | V |

Question 7 Sadly, she walked past the canal boat, which was slowly sinking.

| A | V |

Challenge Answers will vary. Possible answers: Abseil absently; Bewilder bimonthly; Collate continuously; Donate dopily; Emancipate ecstatically; Fester feverishly; Gesticulate grandly; Herald hoarsely; Imagine ignobly; Jet joyously; Knead keenly; Lease legally; Maintain meticulously; Nominate nefariously; Operate offensively; Persevere patiently; Quiver quaintly; Rampage rebelliously; Splutter sporadically; Thwart tranquilly; Undercut undemocratically; Venerate viciously; Withdraw weirdly; X-ray xerographically; Yield yearningly; Zest zealously.

Page 11 Pronouns

Question 1 a) it **b)** them, him **c)** she, it **d)** they, their **e)** it, he **f)** her, he, them, she

Question 2 a) He told him that it was locked. **b)** He lifted them onto it. **c)** She waved goodbye as he

drove away in it. **d)** "Where is it?" he asked. **e)** We went on it.

Question 3 a) his **b)** their **c)** your **d)** they

Challenge Answers will vary. Possible answer: Imran and Gill left Harry Potter on top of the desk.

Page 13 Connectives and conjuctions

Question 1 a) I ran the fastest although my shoes didn't fit properly. **b)** I ran the fastest because I had trained the hardest. **c)** I ran the fastest so I was selected to run the race.

Question 2 Answers will vary. Possible answers: **a)** although / even though / but **b)** when / because / as **c)** but / although / when **d)** so / and

Question 3 (before), (When), (Despite), (and), (Meanwhile), (Now)

Question 4 Answers will vary. Possible answers: **a)** I said I was sorry. **b)** Jake pushed him. **c)** I was doing my maths. **d)** she ran all the way. **e)** Hamil hid the box.

Challenge Answers will vary. For example, you might have a group of connectives that are linked to time: when / after / before / later on.

Page 14 Prepositions

Question 1
a) The cat sat underneath the bed.
b) The cat sat next to the fire.
c) The cat sat between the rows of flowers.

Question 2 Answers will vary. Possible answers: **a)** in / on / next to / behind / inside **b)** next to / in front of / behind / by **c)** on / under / beside **d)** over / around / through

Challenge Answers will vary. Possible answer: Put the box next to the bag that is behind the chair, which is under the table, which is on the rug, which is next to the sofa.

Page 15 Articles

Question 1 a) an arrow **b)** a gate **c)** a house **d)** an hour **e)** an engine **f)** an orange

Question 2
a) Vishnu wanted (a) new cable for his laptop.
b) Some children needed (an) hour or two to complete their task.
c) (The) reason I forgot was because I was rushing.
d) Sarah had forgotten (the) password for her email account.

Page 17 Statements, questions and commands

Question 1

	Question	Command	Statement
Go straight to bed!		✔	
What time is it?	✔		
Don't stop!		✔	
The rabbit hopped.			✔
When can we go?	✔		
The watch was new.			✔
Shut up!		✔	

Question 2 a) ! **b)** ? **c)** . **d)** ? **e)** !

Question 3
Stir the mixture well. → Instructions
The man crept through the castle. → Story
What was the best part of the journey? → Interview
Turn right at the bridge. → Instructions
The flowers waved gently. → Story

Question 4 a) I can go. **b)** Here it is.

Question 5 a) Sit down (now)! **b)** Pass me that (box)! **c)** Tidy up (this mess)!

Challenge Answers will vary. Possible answers: Can I ride my bike? I can ride my bike. Could you have taken the present with you? You could have taken the present with you. Will I go in the car? Will I go in the car.

Page 19 Tenses

Question 1

Past tense	Present tense	Future tense
he ate / was eating	he eats / is eating	he will eat
we watched / were watching	we watch/ are watching	we will watch
she jumped / was jumping	she jumps / is jumping	she will jump
they worked / were working	they work / are working	they will work
you bought / were buying	you buy / are buying	you will buy

Question 2 a) I went / was going to school. **b)** He raced / was racing John. **c)** I saw / could see the moon.

Question 3 a) Jake will be late. **b)** Caitlin will run well. **c)** Stephi will want a drink.

Question 4 a) I watch / am watching the film. **b)** I hear a shout. **c)** I teach / am teaching Rowan to play the piano.

Question 5
past tense – hoped, waved, climbed, grew, kicked
present tense – plead, walk, work, fly
future tense – will laugh, will sew, will dance

Question 6 c)

Challenge Answers will vary. Possible answer: Tomorrow, we will go to Alton Towers, which is that fantastic place where Dad was sick on the roller-coaster

Page 21 Subject and verb agreement

Question 1

Singular verb: He	swims	plays	writes
	races	holds	catches

Plural verb: They	swim	play	write
	race	hold	catch

Question 2 b), d), e) ticked

Question 3 a) is **b)** are **c)** arrive **d)** are **e)** are **f)** sounds

Question 4 a) one sheep drawn **b)** more than one sheep drawn

Question 5 a) Joshua and George *write* well. **b)** The trees *are* too tall. **c)** Where *is* the train? **d)** Immi or the twins *watch* this programme. **e)** Why *are* the children shouting? **f)** The teenagers always *shout* at me.

Challenge Answers will vary. Possible answers: he goes / we go; he cries / we cry

Page 23 I and me

Question 1 a) I **b)** me **c)** I

Question 2

Zia and I went fishing.	✔
Liam came with Conor and me.	✔
Lani and me ate pizza for dinner.	
They presented a cup to Laura and I.	
If Caitlin and I win, we will share the prize with Nye.	✔
Don't ask Eleanor and me to do the tidying up!	✔

A1

Question 3 a) I **b)** I **c)** me **d)** I **e)** me

Question 4 a) I **b)** me **c)** I **d)** I **e)** me

Challenge Answers will vary. Sample answer: During the day, whilst Pat did the chores, Paul and I continued writing. Despite the lure of the sun, she and I persisted with our homework. Corbin and I completed the task. Please give it to Kurt and me. The computer belongs to Sandy and me. Whenever Bob and me remember that time, we shudder. Joe and me went to the beach. How will you know if Ivete and me don't go? It was presented well by Yanqun and I. If it was only up to Charlotte and I, we'd move house tomorrow.

Page 25 Capital letters

Question 1 Answers will vary. Check that capital letters are used correctly.

Question 2 John, Monday, Paris, Spanish, Beauty, Beast, Muslim, I, Savoy Hotel

Question 3 a) Mr Lomas was cross because last Tuesday, at Buxworth, we jumped in the canal. **b)** Last July, the Spanish students enjoyed performing in our concert, The Sea Saga. (Also accept the Sea Saga.) **c)** We walked up Eccles Pike when it snowed last Christmas. **d)** When I talked to Kim she said The Diary of a Dopey Dog was her favourite book.

Question 4 a) foxes, cities, scavenge, bins **b)** train, weekend **c)** day, month, religions, school

Question 5 Next, Pat went to the hospital.

Challenge Answers will vary. Check that capital letters are used correctly in the address.

Page 26 Question marks

Question 1 Accept any relevant question that matches the given answers.

Questions must begin with a capital letter and end with a question mark.

Question 2

a) I have already shown you the newspaper, haven't I?

b) "Didn't you realise it was non-uniform day Jack?" whispered Abid.

Page 27 Exclamation marks

Question 1 a), c) ticked

Question 2 Answers will vary. Possible answers: Open it! To show a command. Unbelievable! To show exasperation.

Page 29 Commas

Question 1 a) "Come here!" shouted the angry farmer. **b)** "The water is really cold," declared Tom. **c)** Olivia asked, "Why did you paint that red?" **d)** "The film is starting," announced the usher. **e)** Joshua whispered, "I've forgotten my homework."

Question 2 a) We packed shorts, tee-shirts, swimsuits and sandals. **b)** He ate sandwiches, crisps, a pie, some cherries and a biscuit. **c)** We bought balloons, streamers, flags and bunting. **d)** The house was big, old, dirty, dark and cold. **e)** A big red monster ate cars, cans, old rugs and an ironing board.

Question 3 a), d) circled

Question 4

a) Push the button, and it will make a sound.

b) When I swim, I like to splash other people.

c) Sam said, "We don't want to go."

d) Buy some milk, bread and cheese after tea.

Question 5 a) "Have a good look," said Charlie, "because you won't see it again." **b)** To raise money for charity, last night I walked, ran, swam and biked. **c)** Bring the football in if you have finished playing. **d)** Barti muttered, "If we do maths, literacy, French and science, I will be shattered!" **e)** When he saw me, he ran off down the road shouting, "Help!"

Challenge Possible answers:

1 To separate items in a list.

2 To separate speech from the speaker, unless a ? or ! is already used.

3 To join two complete sentences when the second sentence begins with and, or, yet, while, but.

4 To insert a phrase into the middle of a sentence (uses two commas).

5 To add a phrase at the beginning or end of the sentence (uses one comma).

Page 31 Apostrophes
Question 1

Question 2 a) can't **b)** we've **c)** I'll **d)** she's **d)** they're **e)** it's

Question 3 a) the girl's hens **b)** my dad's car **c)** Andy's helmet **d)** the sisters' dog **e)** cats run

Question 4 a) one bird had one nest **b)** more than one child had some sweets **c)** more than one car had some wheels

Challenge The boys' playtime was cancelled because they played a trick. It's a good job its victim wasn't a teacher! Anyway, they hid Paul's books in Mrs Berry's bucket. The books' pages weren't very clean afterwards and Ms Moore's response wasn't a happy one. She's frightening when she's cross.

Page 33 Speech marks

Question 1 a) "Don't listen to me," said Mark. **b)** Jac whispered, "Are we safe yet?" **c)** The manager called, "Bring me that bag." **d)** "I need another drink," gasped Louis.

Question 2 a) An exclamation mark is missing from the end of what was said. **b)** A capital letter is needed at the start of the speech. The speech should end with a question mark, not a full stop. **c)** The second inverted commas are in the wrong place; they should follow the comma. **d)** A comma is needed to separate the speaker from the speech. The speech should start with a capital letter.

Question 3 (2 marks for each of the three speakers – 1 mark for putting the inverted commas in the correct place and 1 mark for all the associated punctuation, including a new line for a new speaker.)

"Tom and Barti should be here by now," said Joshua.

"Don't worry," responded Lucy Mae, "I bet they are with Libby."

"No they aren't!" snapped William. "Libby is with Caitlin."

Question 4

	Is it correct?	If no, explain why not.
"Keep your head up," said the swimming teacher.	✔	
Charlie shouted "Help!"		Needs a comma to separate the speaker from the speech.
Annie said, "my hand hurts."		Needs a capital letter to start the speech.
"Give him a chance," pleaded Ona.	✔	
Hayley whispered, "Can you see the fawn?"	✔	
"Go away! shouted" Sam loudly.		The second speech mark should be after the !

Challenge Answers will vary. Possible answers: gulped, smirked, acknowledged, coaxed, gurgled, pondered, snapped, commanded, snarled, commented, hinted, hissed, advised, promised, concluded, confessed, protested, snorted, sobbed, argued, asked, insisted, asserted, interjected, cried, stammered, croaked, crowed, jeered

Page 35 Direct and indirect speech
Question 1

Question 2 Answers will vary. Possible answers: **a)** Dan announced that it was too cold. **b)** James wondered if he could go on the roller-coaster. **c)** Imogen demanded a new bike. **d)** Vani whispered that it was dark. **e)** Grace confessed that she had broken the light.

Question 3 Answers will vary. Possible answers:

Direct speech	Indirect speech
Libby said, "I like that cake."	Libby commented that she liked that cake.
"Did you see John?" asked Kai.	Kai asked if I had seen John.
"Would you like me to wash the car?" offered Nye.	Nye offered to wash the car.
"Lift the lid!" ordered Mr Makarov.	Mr Makarov ordered me to lift the lid.
"It's too expensive!" snapped Gill.	Gill told me it was too expensive.

Question 4 Answers will vary. Possible answers: Andy stated that it was a fantastic phone. Ian explained that his dad had bought it for him. Andy asked to have a look. Ian told him it was OK but not to drop it.

Challenge Answers will vary. Possible answers: threatened, boasted, drawled, moaned, bragged, requested, uttered, retorted, revealed, explained, roared, wailed, warned, gasped, screamed, wept

Page 37 Synonyms

Question 1 Answers will vary. Possible answers: **a)** unpleasant / horrid **b)** starving / famished **c)** gentle / thoughtful **d)** departed / left **e)** sobbed / wailed **f)** vehicle / taxi **g)** banquet / feast **h)** track / walkway **i)** absolutely / certainly **j)** up-to-date / fashionable **k)** pest / irritant

Question 2 One sunny day, a handsome boy visited the fair. He rode on the big wheel before he ventured on the bumper cars. He thought the funfair was wonderful. He departed for home on the bus. It had been a brilliant day for him.

Question 3

honour — reason
awkward — resident
inhabitant — uncomfortable
purpose — respect

Question 4

| see, notice, watch, observe | story, myth, tale, legend | large, huge, enormous, immense | demand, desire, ask, request |
| deny, decline, reject, refuse | dampness, wet, mist, moisture | tough, robust, bold, hardy | speedy, fast, quick, rapid |

Challenge Answers will vary. Possible answers:
a) carnival, event, fair, fiesta **b)** annihilate, demolish, obliterate **c)** confront, contest, dare

Page 39 Antonyms

Question 1 Answers will vary. Possible answers:
a) pleasant / nice **b)** full / satiated **c)** unkind
d) came **e)** laughed **f)** huge **g)** dawdle **h)** down
i) unlikely **j)** ancient **k)** helpful

Question 2 a) When running downhill, the woman was slower than me. She had shorter legs and she loses all the races she enters. **b)** She had short hair and was unkind to nobody. It was inexpensive/cheap to buy her paintings. They were never very unpopular but I didn't have one. **c)** The ugly lady put the cover under the chair after entering the room. She shouted loudly as she opened the door.

Question 3

innocent — uncertain
confident — guilty
legible — ordinary
special — illegible

Question 4 a) late **b)** difficult, complicated
c) lumpy, rough **d)** wonderful, excellent **e)** over, above

Challenge Answers will vary. Possible answers: **a)** doubt certainty, trust, have confidence in, conviction, belief **b)** happy sad, miserable, unhappy, dejected, despondent, downcast, downhearted **c)** smile frown, scowl, glower, glare, grimace

Page 41 Prefixes

Question 1 unkind, mismatch, nonsense, impossible

Question 2 disappear / reappear, discover / uncover / recover, uniform / inform / deform / reform, inactive / reactive, recycle / bicycle / tricycle / unicycle

Question 3 a) contract, standard, divide, marine
b) sleep, work, land, book **c)** number, bid, live, perform

Question 4 Answers will vary. Possible answers:
a) transatlantic, transform, transport
b) misapprehension, missspell, mistake
c) multimillionaire, multiplex, multi-storey

Question 5 a) misplaced **b)** discovered

Question 6 a) below an acceptable standard
b) not a hospitable (friendly) place

Challenge Answers will vary.

Prefix	Meaning	Examples
im–	not	impartial, impatient, improbable
in–	not	indestructible, indirect, indiscreet
mis–	wrong	misplaced, misfired, misunderstood
non–	not	non-return, non-specific, non-starter

pre–	before	presoak, presuppose, pre-war
re–	again	reappear, regain, retest
sub–	under or below	subfloor, subclause, subterranean
super–	above	superman, supernatural, superscript
un–	not	unavailable, unattractive, unfinished

Page 43 Suffixes

Question 1 beauty, gold, music

Question 2 Answers will vary. Possible answers:
thoughtful / thoughtless, soften / softly / softer / softest, timely / timed / timewise / timeless, actively / activate

Question 3 a) listen, walk, work, open **b)** depend, reason, understand, like **c)** help, wish, care, watch

Question 4 Answers will vary. Possible answers:
a) beautify, satisfy, nullify, qualify **b)** hungry, thirsty, achy, shaky **c)** hasten, wooden, golden, lengthen

Question 5 a) later **b)** identify

Question 6 a) a person who sails **b)** holding an equal position to someone else **c)** in a funny way

Challenge: Answers will vary. Possible answers:

Examples may include
dictatorship
minder / curator
politician
electrify
accommodate
lovable / horrible
mindful
smelly
thoughtless
otherwise / downward
calmly

Page 45 Homonyms

Question 1 Their house is near and they're going to be there before dark. Their dad said so.

Question 2 To light a fire you need to rub two sticks together. It's not too hard to do.

Question 3 We raced off to Lea Green with our cases. Lots of us took our teddies as well. There are so many things to do there. Our favourite part was taking our boots off after the walk!

Question 4 The coat, which was shabby, was said to have belonged to a witch, which is probably not true.

Question 5 a) cheep **b)** bare **c)** blew **d)** knight
e) male **f)** piece **g)** meet **h)** grown **i)** great
j) mane **k)** not **l)** rein / reign

Question 6 a) except **b)** fare **c)** he'll **d)** missed
e) scene **f)** break

Challenge Answers will vary. Possible answers:
I'll / isle; beach/ beech; chilli / chilly; currant / current; heard / herd; leak / leek; peace / piece; plain / plane; seam / seem; sloe / slow

Page 47 Silent letters

Question 1 a) wriggle **b)** hymn **c)** science
d) whistle **e)** debt **f)** gnome

Question 2 a) knight **b)** scissors **c)** thumb
d) sandwich **e)** castle **f)** guitar **g)** sword **h)** knife
i) ghost **j)** lamb

Question 3 a) nail **b)** climb **c)** bridge **d)** autumn
e) answer **f)** ballet

Question 4 Answers will vary. Possible answers:

Words that start with a silent k	Words that start with a silent g	Words that end with a silent b	Words that start with a silent w
knead, kneel, knit, knowledge, knock	gnome, gnaw, gnash, gnarl, gnat	comb, tomb, womb, limb, bomb, climb	wriggle, write, wrist, wretch, wreck

Question 5 a) There is an m before the b. **b)** There is an n after the k. **c)** There is an n after the g. **d)** There is an r after the w.

Challenge Answers will vary. Possible answers:
pneumatic, psychology, ptarmigan

Page 49 Plurals
Question 1

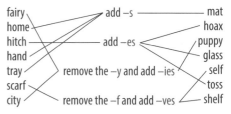

fairy, home, hitch, hand, tray, scarf, city — add –s / add –es / remove the –y and add –ies / remove the –f and add –ves — mat, hoax, puppy, glass, self, toss, shelf

Question 2 a) dishes **b)** trays **c)** elves **d)** watches
e) daisies

Question 3 a) buses **b)** lessons **c)** jellies **d)** calves
e) matches **f)** keys

Challenge Answers will vary. Possible answers:
foot / feet; fungus / fungi; hippopotamus / hippopotami; tooth / teeth; ox / oxen; die / dice

Page 43 Comparative and superlative

Question 1 e) best

Question 2 hottest

Question 3

Adjective	Descriptor	Comparative	Superlative
best			✔
further		✔	
tall	✔		
most frightening			✔
glowing	✔		
healthier		✔	

Question 4

C   C

The hotter the day got, the slower the children ran, but the teacher was the slowest!

S

Question 5 c) circled

Question 6

Adjective	Comparative	Superlative
full	fuller / more full	fullest
mad	madder / more mad	maddest / most mad
jolly	jollier	jolliest

Challenge Answers will vary. Check correct use of comparatives and superlatives.

Page 52 The 'i' before 'e' rule

Question 1 a) thief **b)** friend **c)** height **d)** leisure **e)** /field

Question 2 a) ceiling **b)** receipt **c)** achieve **d)** deceive **e)** relief **f)** priest **g)** deceit **h)** grief
i) niece **j)** shied **k)** conceive **l)** receive

Question 3

(Thier) Their, (Peirce) Pierce, (Niether) Neither, (Shreiked) Shrieked, (Casheir) Cashier, (Seige) Siege

Page 53 –able and –ible

Question 1

readable
acceptable
agreeable
predictable
reasonable
detestable

Question 2

pitiable
reliable
enviable
identifiable
pliable

Question 3 a) horrible inedible. **b)** comfortable, reasonable **c)** sensible, reliable dependable **d)** unacceptable impossible **e)** be flexible.

Page 54 –tion, –cian and –sion

Question 1

Add –tion	Add –cian	Add –sion
attraction	beautician	compassion
equation	politician	possession
fraction	musician	conclusion
mention	technician	version
consideration	physician	expression
collection	optician	mansion
position	mathematician	fusion

Question 2 a) education **b)** decoration **c)** action **d)** inspection **e)** discussion **f)** separation

Question 3 a) station **b)** attention **c)** revision **d)** division

Page 55 Per–, pre– and pro–

Question 1

+per	+pre	+pro
performance	prevent	pronoun
personification	predict	programme
persuade	precise	product
perfume	present	process
percent	prefer	promise
permission	prejudice	problem

Question 2 (perdictable) predictible, (percession) procession, (profer) prefer, (perduce) produce, (proimeter) perimeter

Page 56 De– or di–

Question 1 a) decision **b)** destroyed **c)** discovered **d)** desire **e)** disaster

Question 2 a) disabled **b)** difficult **c)** dignity **d)** despicable **e)** determine **f)** devious **g)** detective **h)** direction **i)** dimension **j)** digit **k)** design **l)** digest

Question 3 descredit, dispise, discourage, devine, desturb

Question 4 Answers will vary. Possible answers:

a) Mum hated it when there was a dilemma amongst the children.

b) Surprisingly, the shopping centre was deserted.

c) Anthony was desperate to score the winning goal.

d) The pizza was burnt and tasted disgusting.

e) Detached house are usually more expensive than semi-detached houses.

Page 57 –ough

Question 1 a) cough **b)** rough **c)** tough **d)** borough **e)** enough **f)** although **g)** trough **h)** plough

Question 2 Answers should be correctly sorted into the spelling jars. **a)** daughter **b)** caught **c)** naughty **d)** fought **e)** taught **f)** fraught **g)** distraught **h)** sought

Question 3 Answers will vary. Possible answers:

a) The doughnut was absolutely delicious. **b)** It rained lots throughout the night.

Page 58 –il, –al, –el and –le

Question 1 –il (stencil, utensil) –al (animal, natural) -el (swivel, squirrel) and –le (people, huddle)

Question 2

a) Rumble **b)** ladle **c)** council **d)** little **e)** numeral **f)** petal **g)** normal **h)** middle **i)** general **j)** loyal **k)** hospital **l)** example **m)** beetle **n)** metal **o)** electrical **p)** possible

Question 3 (doubil) double, (snuggel) snuggle, (cycil) cycle, (saddel) saddle, (uncil) uncle, (giggil) giggle

Page 59 Learning Year 5 and 6 words

Question 2 a) recommend **b)** excellent **c)** opportunity **d)** immediately **e)** existence **f)** secretary **g)** yacht **h)** average **i)** system

Question 3

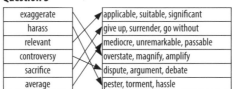

exaggerate		applicable, suitable, significant
harass		give up, surrender, go without
relevant		mediocre, unremarkable, passable
controversy		overstate, magnify, amplify
sacrifice		dispute, argument, debate
average		pester, torment, hassle

Now try these questions:

1 Join the words to the labels to show how these apostrophes are used.

| possessions | That is Kyle's cat.
I can't go.
Here is Pat's key.
They won't know.
It's mine! | omission (contractions) |

(1 mark each)

/5

2 Write these words as contractions with the apostrophes in the correct places.

a) can not _____ **b)** we have _____ **c)** I will _____

d) she is _____ **e)** they are _____ **f)** it is _____

(1 mark each)

/6

3 Put the apostrophes in the correct places to make them match the pictures.

a) **b)**  **c)** **d)** **e)**

the girls hens   my dads car   Andys helmet   the sisters dog   cats run

(1 mark each)

/5

4 Match the phrase to the correct meaning.

a) the bird's nest

| one bird had one nest | one bird had some nests | more than one bird had a nest |

b) the children's sweets

| one child had one sweet | one child had some sweets | more than one child had some sweets |

c) the cars' wheels

| one car had one wheel | one car had some wheels | more than one car had some wheels |

(1 mark each)

/3

CHALLENGE

Copy this paragraph, putting in the missing apostrophes correctly.

The boys playtime was cancelled because they played a trick. Its a good job its victim wasnt a teacher! Anyway, they hid Pauls books in Mrs Berrys bucket. The books pages werent very clean afterwards and Ms Moores response wasnt a happy one. Shes frightening when shes cross.

Speech marks

Definition: Speech marks (sometimes called inverted commas) are punctuation marks that show what somebody said.

Rules for punctuating speech:

1 Put " " around what the speaker says.

2 A new speech sentence starts with a capital letter (even if it is in the middle of another sentence).

3 Separate what was said from the speaker with a comma unless there is already a ? or an !

4 Start a new paragraph if a sentence has a new speaker saying something.

Examples:

"This was interesting," said Mrs Pattison.

The shadow hissed, "Go away!"

"Where are we?" asked Huang.

Let's practise!

Punctuate the speech in this sentence correctly.

The man shouted get out of the way!

(1) Read the question, then read it again. What are you being asked to do?	**Punctuate the speech in the sentence.**
(2) Work out exactly what was said and put " " around the words.	**The man shouted** get out of the way, **so we write:** The man shouted "get out of the way!"
(3) Start the speech sentence with a capital letter.	**The speech sentence starts with** get **so we write that with a capital:** The man shouted "Get out of the way!"
(4) Separate what was said from the speaker with a comma unless there is already a ? or an !	**The man shouted,** "Get out of the way!"

 **TOP TIP** If you find speech punctuation difficult to remember, start by making sure you put in the " ". You can learn and use the rest of the punctuation rules for speech one at a time. **TOP TIP**

Now try these questions:

Achieved?
☺ ☹ ☹

1 Put the inverted commas and punctuation in the correct places in these sentences.
a) Don't listen to me said Mark.
b) Jac whispered are we safe yet?
c) The manager called bring me that bag!
d) I need another drink gasped Louis.

(1 mark for each line)

/4

2 Circle the errors in this speech punctuation.
a) "Give me the chocolate" said Dan.
b) Gary asked, "shall I go next."
c) "Sam didn't finish his work, said Max."
d) The girl snarled "you'll be sorry!"

(1 mark for each line)

/4

3 Rewrite this paragraph, punctuating it correctly.

Tom and Barti should be here by now said Joshua. Don't worry responded Lucy Mae, I bet they are with Libby. No they aren't! snapped William. Libby is with Caitlin.

(6 marks in total)

/6

4 Tick the sentences that are correctly punctuated or explain why they aren't correct.

	Is it correct?	If not, explain why not.
"Keep your head up," said the swimming teacher.		
Charlie shouted "Help!"		
Annie said, "my hand hurts."		
"Give him a chance," pleaded Ona.		
Hayley whispered, "Can you see the fawn?"		
"Go away! shouted" Sam loudly.		

(2 marks for each line)

/12

CHALLENGE List all the words you could use instead of said to make your speech writing more interesting.

Direct and indirect speech

Definitions: Direct speech shows exactly what somebody has said. This is shown with speech marks when written.

Indirect speech tells you what someone else said, thought or felt. It doesn't need speech marks.

When you change direct speech into indirect speech you might need to change:

pronouns	place and time expressions	tenses

You might need to add in extra words such as:

that	if	whether

Let's practise!

Change this direct speech to indirect speech.

"Let's go on the zip wire now,"
suggested Jo.

1	Read the question, then read it again. What are you being asked to do?	**Change the direct speech to indirect speech.**
2	Start the indirect speech with the person.	Jo suggested
3	Check the pronouns.	Let's **is short for** let us. **The** us **needs to change to** we.
4	Check the time and place words.	**We need to change** now **to the past. We could use** then **or** next.
5	Check the tenses.	**We need to change** go **to the past tense –** went.
6	Write the complete answer.	Jo suggested we went on the zip wire next.
7	Say the answer to yourself to check it sounds correct.	**It is fine, but we could add** that. Jo suggested that we went on the zip wire next.

TOP TIP   There is no change to: could, would, should, might and ought.
You can use the present tense in reported speech if you
want to say that something is still true.   **TOP TIP**

Now try these questions:

1 Match these sentences to the correct box.

| indirect speech | "I want that one," said Lani.
Cal said we could come.
Freya called, "Where are you?"
Mr Kwec ordered us to tidy up.
Sally apologised for being late. | direct speech |

(1 mark each)

/5

2 Write one indirect speech word on each line. Only use each word once.

a) Dan _____ that it was too cold.

b) James _____ if he could go on the roller-coaster.

c) Imogen _____ a new bike.

d) Vani _____ that it was dark.

e) Grace _____ that she had broken the light.

(1 mark for each line)

/5

3 Complete the table. The first one is done for you.

Direct speech	Indirect speech
Jack said, " Give it to me."	Jack told me to give it to him.
Libby said, "I like that cake."	
"Did you see John?" asked Kai.	
	Nye offered to wash the car.
"Lift the lid!" ordered Mr Makarov.	
	Gill told me it was too expensive.

(1 mark for each row)

/5

4 Change this conversation to indirect speech.

"What a fantastic phone!" said Andy.
"Yes, my dad bought it for me," explained Ian.
"Can I have a look?" asked Andy.
"Okay, but don't drop it," replied Ian.

(1 mark for each line)

/4

_____

_____

_____

_____

 **CHALLENGE** Write all the words you can think of for indirect speech. Start with said, asked. You might like to use a dictionary or thesaurus to help you.
Use the three most interesting words to write some reported speech sentences.

Synonyms

Definition: Synonyms are words that have the same (or a similar) meaning.
Sets of synonyms make a word family. For example:

> quiet   silent   still   hushed   noiseless   soundless
> tranquil   calm   peaceful

Purpose: Using synonyms avoids repetition and makes your writing more interesting, e.g.:

> said   whispered   hissed   called   shouted   replied   howled   cried

Let's practise!

Match the words that mean the same.

precise	join
regret	exact
unite	beginning
origin	rue

1 Read the question, then read it again. What are you being asked to do?

Match the words with the same meaning.

2 Look for any words where you are certain of the meanings.

Regret means being sorry. **Beginning** means the start. **Origin** means the start. **Unite** means put together.

3 Join up the words that you know match.

Origin and **beginning** both mean start.

4 Work out any other words you can.

Regret means being sorry and neither join nor exact are to do with being sorry, so **rue** must match with regret. **Unite** means put together and that must match with join. That just leaves **precise** and **exact**.

5 Join the matching pairs.

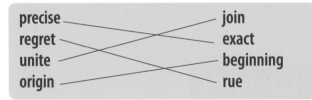

Now try these questions:

1 Write synonyms for these words.

a) nasty _____ b) hungry _____ c) kind _____

d) went _____ e) cried _____ f) car _____

g) meal _____ h) path _____ i) definitely _____

j) modern _____ k) nuisance _____

(1 mark each)

/11

2 Replace the repeated words in this paragraph with synonyms to make the writing more interesting.

One nice day, a nice boy went to the fair. He went on the big wheel before he went on the bumper cars. He thought the funfair was nice. He went home on the bus. It had been a nice day for him.

(1 mark each)

/8

3 Match the words that mean the same.

honour	reason
awkward	resident
inhabitant	uncomfortable
purpose	respect

(1 mark each)

/4

4 Write these words in the correct word family.

immense   observe   moisture   rapid   request
legend   refuse   hardy

see, notice, watch,	story, myth, tale,	large, huge, enormous,	demand, desire, ask,
deny, decline, reject,	dampness, wet, mist,	tough, robust, bold,	speedy, fast, quick,

(1 mark each)

/8

CHALLENGE

Make synonym word families for these words.

a) festival   b) destroy   c) challenge

Use a thesaurus to help you.

Which word was it easiest to find synonyms for?
Why do you think so?

Antonyms

Definition: Antonyms are words that have opposite meanings. You can often make an antonym using a prefix. Other antonyms can be totally different words.

Examples:

Word	Antonym using a prefix	Antonym using a different word
happy	unhappy	miserable
appear	disappear	vanish
perfect	imperfect	flawed
trust	mistrust	suspect

Let's practise!

Match the words that mean the opposite.

extend	unconscious
conscious	melt
darken	reduce
appear	lighten
freeze	disappear

1 Read the question, then read it again. What are they asking you to do?

Match the words with the opposite meaning.

2 Look for any words where the opposite is made with a prefix.

conscious **and** unconscious
appear **and** disappear

3 Join up the words that you know match.

Darken **and** lighten **are opposites.**

4 Think about the words that are left.

That leaves freeze **and** extend. Freeze **and** melt **are opposites, so** reduce **and** extend **must be opposites too.**

5 Join the words that match.

extend	unconscious
conscious	melt
darken	reduce
appear	lighten
freeze	disappear

TOP TIP   Antonyms can be used for different classes of words.
verbs (open – shut)   adjectives (angry – calm)
adverbs (suddenly – gradually)   prepositions (over – under)   **TOP TIP**

Now try these questions:

1 Write antonyms for these words.

a) nasty _____ b) hungry _____ c) kind _____

d) went _____ e) cried _____ f) tiny _____

g) rush _____ h) up _____ i) likely _____

j) modern _____ k) nuisance _____

(1 mark each)

/11

2 Replace each word in red with an antonym.

a) When running uphill, the man was faster than me. He had longer legs and he wins all the races he enters.

_____

b) He had long hair and was kind to everybody. It was expensive to buy his paintings. They were always very popular but I didn't have one.

_____

(1 mark each)

/3

c) The beautiful lady put the cover over the chair before leaving the room. She whispered softly as she shut the door.

_____

3 Match the words that mean the opposite. The first one has been done for you.

real	uncertain
innocent	guilty
confident	artificial
legible	ordinary
special	illegible

(1 mark each)

/4

4 Circle all the words which are antonyms of the first word.

a) early   momentary   late   morning   night

b) simple   difficult   easy   complicated   frightening

c) smooth   shake   lumpy   rough   shiny

d) terrible   wonderful   excellent   nasty   terrifying

e) under   over   below   beneath   submarine   above

(1 mark each)

/5

CHALLENGE

Write all the antonyms you can for these words.

a) doubt   b) happy   c) smile

Use a thesaurus and a dictionary to help you.

Prefixes

Definition: A prefix is a group of letters placed at the start of a word.

Purpose: The prefix changes the meaning of the word. Knowing prefixes can make spelling easier and increase your vocabulary.

Some common prefixes with their meanings are:

Prefix	Meaning	Examples
dis–	not or away	disadvantage, disconnect, dismount
en–	make or put into	enable, enact, endanger
im–	not	immature, impossible
in–	not	inhuman, insane
mis–	wrong	mistake, misspell
non–	not	non-existent, non-fiction
pre–	before	prehistoric, pre-shrink
re–	again	redesign, reconsider, repaint
sub–	under or below	submarine, subsoil, substandard
super–	above	superhuman, supervisor
un–	not	uncertain, unfinished, unhappy

Let's practise!

Match the prefixes and the words to make the words mean the opposite.

Prefixes: non– mis– dis– im– in– un–
Words: appear probable judgemental

(1) Read the question, then read it again. What are you being asked to do?

> Make the words mean the opposite.

(2) Look at the first word and think of its opposite.

> **appear** The opposite of appear is disappear.

(3) Look at the next word and think of its opposite.

> **probable** The opposite of probable is improbable.

(4) Look at the last word and think of its opposite.

> **judgemental** The opposite of judgemental is non-judgemental.

(5) Match the prefixes to the words.

> **Prefixes:** non–   mis–   dis–   im–   in–   un–
>
> **Words:**   appear   probable   judgemental

Now try these questions:

1 What prefix would you put at the beginning of each word to make it mean the opposite?

_____ kind _____ match _____ sense _____ possible

2 Find two prefixes for each of these words that would make a different word.

_____ appear _____ cover _____ form _____ active _____ cycle
_____ appear _____ cover _____ form _____ active _____ cycle

3 Circle the four words in each line that could go with the prefix to make new words.

a) sub– contract reason standard divide active marine demand
b) over– sleep care work land device read book
c) out– number form sleep wish bid live perform

4 Think of three new words that start with each of these prefixes.

a) trans– _____ _____ _____
b) mis– _____ _____ _____
c) multi– _____ _____ _____

5 Write the missing word on the line to complete each sentence correctly.

a) Jack had _____ his glasses; he couldn't find them anywhere.

misplaced   displaced   implaced   nonplaced

b) Columbus went on a voyage and _____ new countries.

recovered   uncovered   miscovered   discovered

6 Write the meaning of each word.

a) substandard _____
b) inhospitable _____

CHALLENGE

Make a prefix table, like the one below, and fill it in using different prefixes.

Prefix	Meaning	Examples
dis–	not *or* away	displease, disrespect
en–	make *or* put into	encircle, endear, enforce

41

Suffixes

Definition: A suffix is a group of letters placed at the end of a word.

Purpose: The suffix adds to the meaning of the word. Knowing suffixes can make spelling easier and increase your vocabulary.

Beware – some suffixes change the spelling of the word!

Examples:

Suffix	Makes	Meaning	Examples
–ship	noun	position held	headship
–er / –or		one who	teacher / orator
–ian		person	magician
–ify	verb	make or become	terrify
–ate		become	irritate
–able / –ible	adjective	capable of being	comfortable / terrible
–ful		full of	beautiful
–y		having	hungry
–less		without	colourless
–wise / –ward	adverb	in the direction or manner of	timewise / homeward
–ly		in that way	quickly

Let's practise!

Change this word twice by adding different suffixes. Write the meanings of the words you have made.

joy

1 Read the question, then read it again. What are you being asked to do?

Make new words by adding a suffix and explain the meanings.

2 Look at the word and find suffixes that would fit onto it.

joy – **ful** and **less** would both work.

3 Think about the meaning of the words.

joyful – **ful** means full of, so joyful means full of joy.

joyless – **less** means without, so joyless means without any joy.

ADDING SUFFIXES

TOP TIP

For one-syllable words ending with a single vowel and consonant, always double the last consonant before adding a suffix that begins with a vowel. For example: winner, flatten, sloppy.

If the word ends in a double vowel or double consonant, do not double the last consonant. For example: shouted, comfortable, mindless, actor.

If a word ends in e, drop the e before adding a suffix that starts with a vowel. For example: tasting, cycled, racer, but not for hopeful and homeless!

TOP TIP

Now try these questions:

1 Remove the suffix and write the root word (the word that the suffix was added to originally) correctly.

(1 mark each)

/3

beautiful _____	golden _____	musician _____

2 Find two suffixes for each of these words that would make a different word.

(1 mark each)

/8

thought _____	soft _____	time _____	active _____
thought _____	soft _____	time _____	active _____

3 Circle the four words in each line that would go with the suffix to make new words.

a) –er   listen   hair   walk   work   hand   clock   open

b) –able   depend   care   reason   thought   understand   like

c) –ful   help   wish   have   care   like   watch

(1 mark each)

/12

4 Write three different words that end with each of these suffixes.

a) –ify   _____   _____   _____

b) –y   _____   _____   _____

c) –en   _____   _____   _____

(1 mark for 2 correct words or 2 marks for 3 correct words each line)

/6

5 Write the missing word on the line to complete each sentence correctly.

a) The plane landed _____ than expected.

   latest   lately   later   lator

b) Every person had to _____ themselves.

   identible   identity   identify   identiate

(1 mark for each line)

/2

6 Write the meaning of each word.

a) sailor   _____

b) partnership   _____

c) funnily   _____

(1 mark for each line)

/3

CHALLENGE

Make another suffix table and fill it in using different examples to those in the table on page 42.

Suffix	Makes	Meaning	Examples
–ship	noun	position held	
–er / –or		one who	
–ian		person	

Homonyms

Definition: Homonyms are words that are spelled or sound the same but have different meanings.

Examples:

Homonyms	Meaning	Homonyms	Meaning
there	can be replaced with here	to	where you are going or what you are doing
they're	is a contraction of 'they are'	too	as well; too many
their	belongs to them	two	the number 2
be	in a state of; to be	see	what you do with your eyes
bee	a flying insect	sea	a large body of water

Let's practise!

Fill in the gaps correctly using **there**, **their** and **they're**.

[1] _____ trip was a disaster! [2] _____ was a storm, [3] _____ coach broke down and now [4] _____ all soaked.

(1) Read the question, then read it again. What are you being asked to do?

Fill the gaps correctly with there, their and they're.

(2) Look at gap 1.

_____ **trip, – it was a trip that belonged to them, so we use their.**

(3) Look at gap 2.

_____ **was could be written as here was so we use there.**

(4) Look at gap 3.

_____ **coach – it was a coach that belonged to them, so we use their.**

(5) Look at gap 4.

_____ **all soaked – they are all soaked, so we use they're.**

(6) Complete the answer.

Their trip was a disaster! There was a storm, their coach broke down and now they're all soaked.

Learn as many homonyms as you can, and watch out for other commonly mixed-up words that aren't homonyms.
Think about quite and quiet.
quite = a little bit   quiet = not noisy

Now try these questions:

1 Fill in the gaps correctly using there, their and they're.

_____ house is near and _____ going to be _____ before dark. _____ dad said so.

(1 mark each)

/4

2 Fill in the gaps correctly using to, too and two.

_____ light a fire you need _____ rub _____ sticks together. It's not _____ hard _____ do.

(1 mark each)

/5

3 Fill in the gaps correctly using of, off, are and our.

We raced _____ to Lea Green with _____ cases. Lots _____ us took _____ teddies as well. There _____ so many things to do there. _____ favourite part was taking _____ boots _____ after the walk!

(1 mark each)

/8

4 Fill in the gaps correctly using witch and which.

The coat, _____ was shabby, was said to have belonged to a _____, _____ is probably not true.

(1 mark each)

/3

5 Write a homonym for each of these words.

a) cheap_____ b) bear _____ c) blue _____ d) night _____
e) mail _____ f) peace _____ g) meat _____ h) groan_____
i) grate _____ j) main _____ k) knot _____ l) rain _____

(1 mark each)

/12

6 Choose the correct word to fill each gap.

a) Everyone _____ Isobel went to the zoo. (accept / except)

b) The train _____ was very expensive. (fair / fare)

c) If Tom is late, _____ be in a lot of trouble. (he'll / heel / heal)

d) Jac _____ the last bus. (missed / mist)

e) The _____ in the school play was hilarious. (scene / seen)

f) Eleanor didn't mean to _____ the window. (brake / break)

(1 mark for each line)

/6

CHALLENGE

List as many homonym pairs as you can. Use a dictionary or thesaurus to help.

Silent letters

Definition: Some words have letters that make no sound. These are called silent letters.

Silent letters are sometimes there because:

a) words used to be said differently in the past

b) words have been borrowed from other languages

c) they show long vowels.

Examples:

Silent letters at the beginning of words	Silent letters within words	Silent letters at the end of words
knee, knife, gnaw, gnat, wrong, write, knight, hour	scissors, league, island, thistle, sign, guess, listen	lamb, solemn, autumn

Let's practise!

Circle the silent letters in these words:

listen   scissors   comb   wrench   knot

(1) Read the question, then read it again. What are you being asked to do?	**Circle the silent letters.**
(2) Say each word carefully, then read each sound as it is written.	listen is l-i-s-t-e-n scissors is s-c-i-s-s-o-r-s comb is c-o-m-b wrench is w-r-e-n-c-h knot is k-n-o-t
(3) Put the sounds together to see which is not sounded in the word.	l-i-s-t-e-n **doesn't sound the** t s-c-i-s-s-o-r-s **doesn't sound the** c c-o-m-b **doesn't sound the** b w-r-e-n-c-h **doesn't sound the** w k-n-o-t **doesn't sound the** k
(4) Circle the silent letters.	**lis͜ten sc͜issors com͜b w͜rench k͜not**
(5) Read the words again to check your answer.	**The answer is correct.**

TOP TIP   To help you remember how to spell a word with a silent letter, say the word stressing the silent letter and break it up into syllables. For example, say:

Feb-ru-ary

emphasising the second syllable.   **TOP TIP**

Now try these questions:

1 Circle the silent letters in these words.

a) wriggle **b)** hymn **c)** science **d)** whistle **e)** debt **f)** gnome

(1 mark each) /6

2 Label these pictures, which are all objects spelled with silent letters.

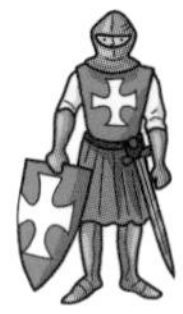

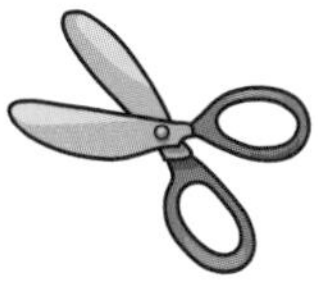

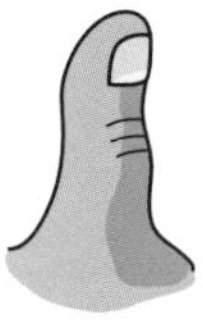

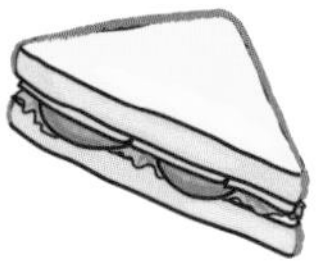

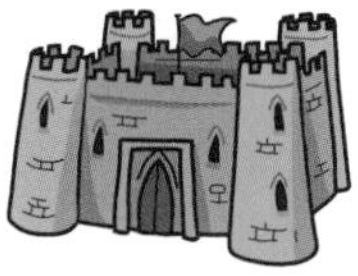

a) ________ b) ________ c) ________ d) ________ e) ________

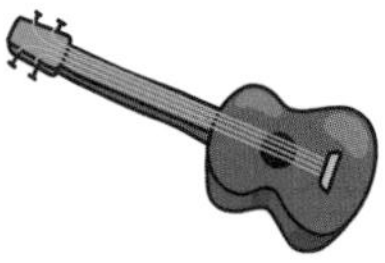

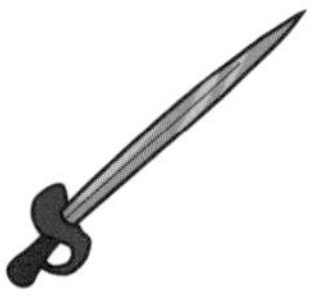

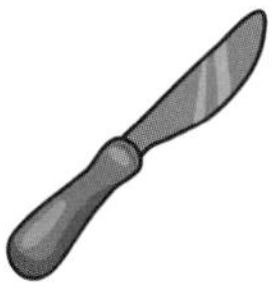

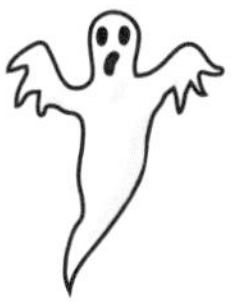

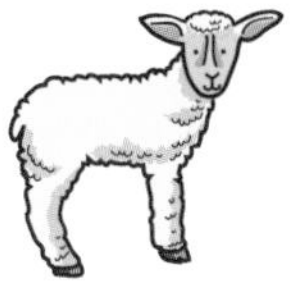

f) ________ g) ________ h) ________ i) ________ j) ________

(1 mark each) /10

3 Circle the correct spelling of each word.

a) knail nail **b)** climb clime **c)** brige bridge
d) autumn autum **e)** anser answer **f)** ballet ballay

(1 mark each) /6

4 Write at least four words in each box.

Words that start with a silent k	Words that start with a silent g	Words that end with a silent b	Words that start with a silent w

(1 mark for each box) /4

5 What do you notice about words that:

a) end with a silent b? ________
b) start with a silent k? ________
c) start with a silent g? ________
d) start with a silent w? ________

(1 mark for each line) /4

CHALLENGE

p is usually silent with n, s and t at the start of a word. This is because these words come from Greek. Use a dictionary to find some of these words and write their meanings.

Achieved? ☺ 😐 ☹

Plurals

Definition: Plurals are nouns that name more than one of something.

Some common ways to make plurals:

Word type	Making the plural	Examples	Exceptions to the rule
Most words	Add –s to the word	dogs, schools, books, houses	Lots – see the other rules!
Words that end in –s, –ss, –ch, –sh, –x, –z	Add –es to the word	matches, pushes, boxes, losses, fizzes	
Words that end in –f	Change the –f to –v and add –es	loaves, hooves, calves	roofs, dwarfs, chiefs
Words that end in –y	Change the –y to –i and add –es	ladies, stories, ponies	words that end in -ey (keys, donkeys, monkeys), and some that end in –ay (days, trays)
Words that end with a consonant and –o	Add –es	tomatoes, volcanoes, potatoes	pianos, halos, solos

Let's practise!
Circle the plurals that are spelled correctly.

Word	wish	half	ditch	turkey	fox	party
Plural	wishes	halfs	ditchs	turkeys	foxes	parties

1 Read the question, then read it again. What are you being asked to do?

Circle the words that are spelled correctly.

2 Look for the words that end in –s, –ss, –ch, –sh, –x or –z.

wish, ditch and fox

3 Check that these plurals end in –es.

wishes and foxes do, so circle those. ditchs doesn't so it shouldn't be circled.

4 Check for words that end in –f.

half

5 Check that these plurals end in –ves.

halfs – no, so it shouldn't be circled.

6 Check for words that end in –y.

turkey and party.

7 Check these plurals end in –ies.

parties does, so circle it. turkey ends in –ey so the –y shouldn't change to i which means it is spelled as turkeys, so circle it.

TOP TIP   Learn words that are exceptions to the rule.   **TOP TIP**

Now try these questions:

1 Join each words to the rule for making the plural.

fairy	add –s	mat
home		hoax
hitch	add –es	puppy
hand		glass
tray	remove the –y and add –ies	self
scarf		toss
city	remove the –f and add –ves	shelf

(1 mark each)

/14

2 Circle the correct plural for the first word in each line.

a) **dish** dishs dishes dishies

b) **tray** traies trayes trays

c) **elf** elves elfies elfs

d) **watch** watchies watchs watches

e) **daisy** daisies daisyies daisys

(1 mark for each line)

/5

3 Write the plural correctly to fill each gap. The first one is done for you.

a) The *buses* were late arriving. (bus)

b) Class 3 had _____ all day. (lesson)

c) Libby made _____ for the class party. (jelly)

d) When Joshua goes home, he helps with the _____. (calf)

e) The _____ in the box were damp so they wouldn't light. (match)

f) Nye lost the _____ to the house. (key)

(1 mark for each line)

/5

CHALLENGE

Some plurals don't have an –s on the end. Think about these pairs:

child – children   man – men   goose – geese

These plurals are called irregular plurals.

How many words with irregular plurals can you find?

Make a list.

Comparative and superlative

Definition: Adjectives that compare two or more things – and can say how super they are!

Comparative: The comparative compares two things and usually ends in –er or uses the word more.

> The tree is taller than the house.
> He is more confident than I am.

Superlative: The superlative compares three or more things and usually ends in –est or uses the word most.

> The red car is faster than the blue, but the yellow car is the fastest.
> It is the most expensive camera I've ever used.

Let's practise!
Circle the sentence which is correct.

a) Bartosz is faster than Joe.

b) Bartosz is fastest than Joe.

c) Bartosz is more faster than Joe.

1 Read the question, then read it again. What are you being asked to do?

Find the correct word(s) for comparing speed.

2 Think about how many things are being compared.

Two people – Bartosz and Joe.

3 Work out the form you need.

Comparing two means we need to use the comparative form using –er or more.

4 Check the options.

It must be a) or c) – they are comparative. c) has more and –er so it must be a).

5 Read the answer to check it sounds correct.

Bartosz is faster than Joe.

Exceptions: irregular adjectives

Descriptor	Comparative form	Superlative form
good	better	best
bad	worse	worst
far	farther / further	farthest / furthest
little	less	least
many	more	most

Comparatives are often used with the word than.

Today is hotter than yesterday.

This book is better than that one.

She is friendlier now than she was before.

Now try these questions:

1 Circle the word or phrase that completes this sentence.

Jack was _____ at running.

a) bestest **b)** most good **c)** goodest **d)** goodiest **e)** best

(1 mark)

/1

2 Underline the word or phrase that completes this sentence.

All the children were hot but Abdul was _____ .

(hotter / hottest / hottier / more hot)

(1 mark)

/1

3 Tick the correct boxes to show the types of adjective.

Adjective	Descriptor	Comparative	Superlative
best			
further			
tall			
most frightening			
glowing			
healthier			

(1 mark each)

/6

4 For comparatives put a C in the box, for superlatives put an S in the box.

The hotter the day got, the slower the children ran, but the teacher was the slowest!

(1 mark each)

/3

5 Circle the sentence that is correct.
a) The country was most peaceful than the city.
b) The country was peacefuller than the city.
c) The country was more peaceful than the city.
d) The country was peacest than the city.

(1 mark)

/1

6 Complete the table by writing the correct word in each box.

Adjective	Comparative	Superlative
		fullest
mad		
	jollier	

(1 mark each box)

/6

Find five exciting adjectives (you could use a dictionary). Write the comparative and superlative forms of the adjective.
Write the most creative sentences you can using these words.

The 'i' before 'e' rule

Many words contain the letters 'i' and 'e' together and you can use this rule to decide whether 'i' comes before 'e' or after it.

'i' before 'e' except after 'c'.

Examples of words that follow the rule:
believe   receive   piece   perceive

Examples of some of the exceptions:
weird   seize   scientific

Some words break the 'i' before 'e' rule and there are some exceptions you need to learn.

Now try these questions:

Achieved?
😊 😐 ☹️

1 Choose the correct spelling of each word pair and write your choice in the space below.

(1 mark each)

/5

a) The shopkeeper suspected the man was a thief/theif. _____
b) I bought my freind/friend a present for her birthday. _____
c) My Dad measures my height/hieght every six months. _____
d) A new leisure/liesure centre has just opened in my town. _____
e) We played games on the feild/field today. _____

2 Write 'ie' or 'ei' in the space to complete each word.

(1 mark each)

/12

a) c____ling   b) rec____pt   c) ach ____ve
d) dec____ve   e) rel ____f   f) pr____st
g) dec____t   h) gr ____f   i) n ____ce
j) sh____ld   k) conc____ve   l) rec____ve

3 Circle the words in the box that are spelled incorrectly and write the correct spellings on the lines.

Mischief Thier Sleigh
Patient Peirce Niether
Vein Fielder Shreiked
Casheir Freight Brief
seige

_____
_____
_____
_____
_____

(1 mark each)

/6

–able and –ible

The –able ending is far more common than the –ible ending.

The –ible ending is used if a complete root word cannot be heard before it.

Now try these questions:

1 Add –able to each of these words to make a new word.

(1 mark each)

/5

Base word	+able	New word
read	+able	readable
accept		
agree		
predict		
reason		
detest		

2 When the base word ends with a 'y', for example 'vary', change the 'y' to an 'i' and then add –able vary –var<u>iable</u>

Base word	Change the 'y' to an 'i'	+able	New word
pity			
rely			
envy			
identify			
ply			

(1 mark each)

/5

3 Choose either –able or –ible to end each of the adjectives. Use a dictionary if you are not sure.

a) When the meal arrived it smelled horr_____and looked ined_____.

b) The chair was very comfort_____and the price was reason _____too!

c) Mrs Morris is looking for a sens_____, reli_____and depend_____ person to be on the school council.

d) The behavior was unaccept_____and it was imposs_____to give anybody a sticker.

e) To be a successful gymnast, you will need to be flex_____.

(1 mark each)

/5

-tion, -cian and -sion

The 'shun' sound at the end of words can be spelled in several different ways.

-tion as in 'motion', -cian as in 'magician' and -sion as in 'profession'. Words that end in -cian often name people.

Now try these questions:

1 Complete the table, adding -tion, -cian and -sion

Add -tion	Add -cian	Add -sion
attrac	beauti	compas
equa	politi	posses
frac	musi	conclu
men	techni	ver
considera	physi	expres
collec	opti	man
posi	mathemati	fu

(1 mark each)

/7

2 Add the suffix **-sion** or **-tion** to the following words to make new words. If the word ends in **e**, remember to drop the **e** before adding the ending

a) Educate _____

b) decorate _____

c) act _____

d) inspect _____

e) discuss _____

f) separate _____

(1 mark each)

/6

3 Write the correct spelling of each word pair on the line.

a) I was waiting at the train station/stashun for a long time.

_____

b) You must pay attension/attention to your teachers.

_____

(1 mark each)

/4

c) It is a good idea to do some revician/revision before a test.

_____

d) The inverse of multiplication is division/divition. _____

TOP TIP ▶ There are some exceptions that do not follow any rules such as ocean and Asian, which you will need to learn. ◀ TOP TIP

Per–, pre– and pro–

Per–, pre– and pro– all sound very similar at the beginning of words. Pronounce the words clearly and this may help you to spell them correctly.

Examples:
perform   pretend   protest

Now try these questions:

1 Complete the table by adding the per–, pre– and pro–.

+per	+pre	+pro
_____formance	_____ vent	_____ noun
_____sonification	_____ dict	_____gramme
_____suade	_____ cise	_____duct
_____fume	_____ sent	_____cess
_____cent	_____ fer	_____mise
_____mission	_____ judice	_____blem

2 Circle the words in the box that are spelled incorrectly and write the correct spellings on the lines.

perdictable	prohibit
percession	promote
prescribe	profer
prehistoric	precious
probably	perduce
profile	perspire
personality	proimeter

_____

_____

_____

_____

_____

_____

De- or di-

The prefix de- usually means 'out of' or 'away from'.

De- or di-? It is sometimes difficult to decide which spelling to use.

The prefix di- usually means 'two' and sometimes di- can be short for 'dis'.

Now try these questions:

Achieved?
☺ ☹ ☹

1 Choose the correct spelling of each word pair and write your choice in the space below.

a) I had a difficult decision/dicision to make. _____

b) The forest fire distroyed/destroyed many trees. _____

c) I discovered/descovered how to change the Internet settings. _____

d) My brother has a strong disire/desire to travel around the world. _____

e) It would be a complete disaster/desaster if you dropped that. _____

(1 mark each)

/5

2 Write de- or di- on each line to complete each word.

a) _____sabled   b) _____fficult   c) _____ gnity

d) _____spicable   e) _____termine   f) _____vious

g) _____tective   h) _____rection   i) _____mension

j) _____ git   k) _____sign   l) _____gest

(1 mark each)

/6

3 Circle the five words that are spelled incorrectly.

| disconnected   descredit   dispise   devastate   destiny |
| descourage   disappear   devine   desturb |

(1 mark each)

/5

4 Write a sentences that includes the following words.

a) dilemma _____

b) deserted _____

c) desperate _____

d) disgusting _____

e) detached _____

(1 mark each)

/5

–ough

The spelling –ough has lots of different sounds.

For example: cough/off, dough/oh, through/oo, plough/ow, thorough/ uh, tough/uff.

Now try these questions:

Achieved?
☺ ☺ ☹

1 Add –ough to complete the spelling of each word.

(1 mark each)

/8

a) C _____   b) r_____   **c)** t _____

d) bor _____   **e)** en_____   **f)** alth_____

g) tr _____   **h)** pl_____

TOP TIP ▶   You will also need to know when to use –ought and –aught.   ◀ **TOP TIP**

2 Complete the following words with –ought or –aught and write them in the correct spelling jar.

a) d_____ er   **b)** c_____   **c)** n_____y

d) f _____   **e)** t _____   **f)** fr_____

(1 mark each)

/8

g) distr_____   **h)** s _____

–ought

–aught

3 Write sentences using the following words.

(1 mark each)

/2

a) doughnut _____

_____

b) throughout_____

_____

–il, –al, –el and –le

Words ending with –il, (pencil) –al, (medal) –el (tunnel) and –le (puddle) often have the same sound.

You could picture the word in your mind, learn the word or look in a dictionary. Sometimes writing the word a couple of different ways can help you to decide which ending looks right.

Achieved?
☺☻☹

Now try these questions:

1 Read the words and sort them into the correct spelling jar.

> animal   people   stencil   swivel   huddle   natural
> utensil   squirrel

(1 mark each)

/8

–il | –al | –el | –le

2 Complete the following words with –il, –al, –el and –le
a) rumb ___   b) lad___   c) counc___   d) litt ___
e) numer___   f) pet ___   g) norm___   h) midd___
i) gener ___   j) loy ___   k) hospit ___   l) examp ___
m) beet___   n) met ___   o) electric___   p) possib___

(1 mark each)

/16

3 Circle the words in the box that are spelled incorrectly and write the correct spellings on the lines.

> doubil   marble   multiple
> snuggel   cycil   whistle
> sandal   saddel   uncil
> gruel   doddle   giggil

_____

_____

_____

_____

(1 mark each)

/6

Learning Years 5 and 6 words

1 Practice writing and spelling the following words.

Word	Look	Cover	Say	Check
parliament				
twelfth				
relevant				
existence				
convenience				
definite				
average				
amateur				

2 Underline the word that is spelt correctly in each line.

a) recomend   reccommend   recommend

b) egcellent   excellent   excellant

c) opportunity   oportunity   opertunity

d) immediateley   immediately   immidiately

e) existance   existence   existience

f) secretery   secritary   secretary

g) yacht   yacth   yoht

h) average   averige   averege

i) sistem   system   systam

3 Match each word to a word family that means the same (synonym).

exaggerate	applicable, suitable, significant
harass	give up, surrender, go without
relevant	mediocre, unremarkable, passable
controversy	overstate, magnify, amplify
sacrifice	dispute, argument, debate
average	pester, torment, hassle

Spelling word list for Years 5 and 6

accommodate

accompany

according

achieve

aggressive

amateur

ancient

apparent

appreciate

attached

available

average

awkward

bargain

bruise

category

cemetery

committee

communicate

community

competition

conscience*

conscious*

controversy

convenience

correspond

criticise (critic + ise)

curiosity

definite

desperate

determined

develop

dictionary

disastrous

embarrass

environment

equip (–ped, –ment)

especially

exaggerate

excellent

existence

explanation

familiar

foreign

forty

frequently

government

guarantee

harass

hindrance

identity

immediate(ly)

individual

interfere

interrupt

language

leisure

lightning

marvellous

mischievous

muscle

necessary

neighbour

nuisance

occupy

occur

opportunity

parliament

persuade

physical

prejudice

privilege

profession

programme

pronunciation

queue

recognise

recommend

relevant

restaurant

rhyme

rhythm

sacrifice

secretary

shoulder

sincere(ly)

soldier

stomach

sufficient

suggest

symbol

system

temperature

thorough

twelfth

variety

vegetable

vehicle

yacht

Many of these words can be used for practice in adding suffixes.

*Conscience and conscious are related to science – all come from the Latin word meaning 'to know'. Conscience is simply science with the prefix con– added. Conscious also contains the 'sci' of science.